TiGER-TiME
FOR STANLEY

TIGER-TIME
FOR STANLEY

BY GRIFF

SCHOLASTIC INC.
New York   Toronto   London   Auckland   Sydney
Mexico City   New Delhi   Hong Kong   Buenos Aires

For little Katy Byrne (x),
... the original Stanley.

ISBN   0-439-28711-1

12 11 10 9 8 7 6 5 4 3 2 1   1 2 3 4 5 6/0

Printed in the U.S.A.   14

First Scholastic printing, March 2002

This is Stanley.
Stanley has a *thing*
about shrimps.

If Stanley were an
animal, he would
be a shrimp ...

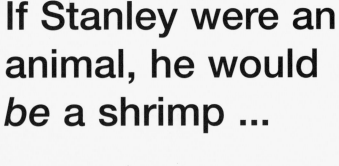

... or a shark,

... or an ant,

... or a caterpillar,

... or a bat,

... or a snail,

... or a **tiger**!

There's only one thing Stanley loves more than his tiger feet ...

And that's Elsie.

Elsie is Stanley's pet cat.

Stanley likes to think of her as his own little tiger. After all ...

In many ways, Elsie is very like a tiger.

Tigers and cats have

sharp, retractable claws

to tear things up!

They both use
their tongues to
clean themselves!

(And sometimes
each other!)

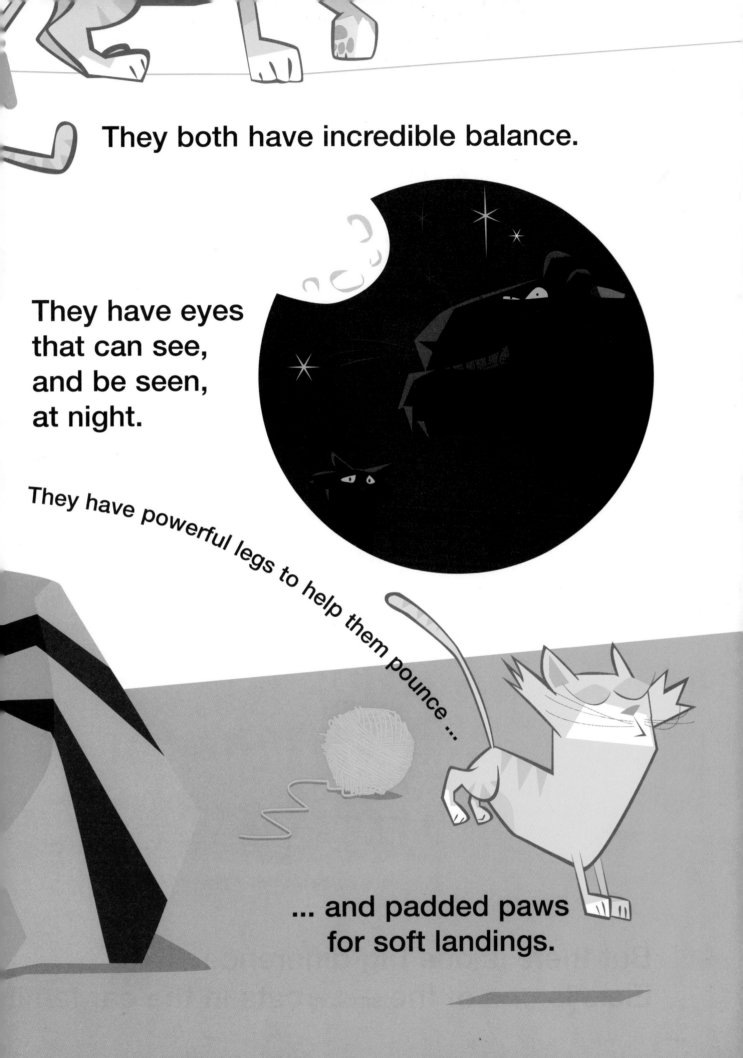

They both have incredible balance.

They have eyes
that can see,
and be seen,
at night.

They have powerful legs to help them pounce ...

... and padded paws
for soft landings.

Elsie even looks and behaves (a bit) like a tiger!

All cats have razor-sharp teeth to help them tear up their food!

They have amazing ears that can turn in different directions. (Not easy!)

They both have super-sensitive noses, which smell three times better than a human (even if Elsie's litter tray doesn't).

They both bury their poop!

THIS IS NOT TRUE: cats bury their poop, but tigers leave theirs wherever they like!

They both have stripes to help them hide when they're hunting.

They both have long tails, which they wag when they're upset.

But there is one **big** difference.
Elsie is one of the smallest cats in the cat family

They both have wiry whiskers to help them 'feel' their way through narrow places.

They both wear warm coats, in every kind of weather.

They can both be a home to tiny fleas!

a tiger is the **largest!**

Elsie sleeps while Stanley
studies tigers.

In fact, she likes to sleep
no matter *what* Stanley's doing.

Sometimes Elsie sleeps so much,
Stanley wonders if a **tiger** might
be a more exciting pet.

Sometimes, Stanley calls Elsie but she doesn't *seem* to hear him.

A tiger has very good hearing
and would **always** come running!

Elsie **hates** water,
especially at bathtime.

Tigers **love** water and
are very good swimmers.

Elsie looks after her kittens by carrying them in her mouth.

A tiger could
carry more
than just a
tiny kitten.

Elsie is scared of even the littlest of dogs.

A tiger isn't
scared of
anything,
no matter
how big!

On the other hand,

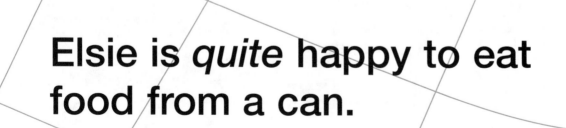

Elsie is *quite* happy to eat food from a can.

A tiger
would need
something
fresher ...

A **whole lot** fresher!

Elsie is happy to play in Stanley's garden.

A tiger would need somewhere bigger ...

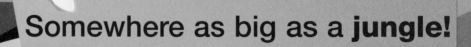

Somewhere as big as a **jungle!**

Elsie *purrs* when Stanley strokes her.

A tiger wouldn't purr, it would ...

ROAR!

Stanley changes
his mind.

Who wants a grumpy old tiger for a pet when Elsie's around?

And besides ...

... tigers are too big for cat doors!

tail end